We are
GIRLS

Claire
and the
Colossal
Treehouse

BONNEY PRESS

Published by Bonney Press,
an imprint of Hinkler Books Pty Ltd 2019
45–55 Fairchild Street
Heatherton Victoria 3202 Australia
www.hinkler.com

BONNEY
PRESS

Story by Katie Hewat
Biographies by Debra Thomas
Illustrations by Olya Badulina

Editorial: Emily Murray
Design: Bianca Zuccolo
Publishing Manager: Jennifer Bilos
Prepress: Splitting Image

ISBN: 978 1 4889 6881 5

Printed and bound in China

Claire
and the
Colossal Treehouse

Katie Hewat

Olya Badulina

There's something inside me I just can't define
that drives me to build and make and design.

I see beauty in buildings; I'm inspired by shapes,
by windows and woodwork, by cushions and drapes.

Frames and dollhouses, swings and hatstands,
I dream my designs, then I work with my hands.

But now my dream's grander than ever before.
It's big and it's bold; it's colossal for sure!

I'll build the best treehouse that I've ever seen.
A palace that's awesome – and I'll be its queen!

I get out my sketch sheets and start on my drawing –
this place won't be average, or normal, or boring.

Up high in the sky with
two stunning towers,

a painted front door

and window-box flowers.

Ceilings that soar and
glass window panes,

and shutters that keep
out the wind and the rain.

With fun hidey-holes and small secret nooks,
and space for a sofa and shelves for my books.

There'll be a long ladder to climb to the top

and railings all round so I'm safe from the drop.

But first I need money for timber and such.
So, how will I ever come up with so much?

I like to work hard, and I know there's a way:
I'll do jobs for some people who'll be happy to pay!

So in summer I sell lemonade by the lake
and buy all my wood with the money I make!

I mow lawns and rake leaves in the baking hot sun,

which earns me enough to buy nails by the ton.

In autumn I walk my aunt's dogs, Rex and Honey,
in exchange for some paint instead of the money.

I scrub and I clean my neighbour's huge pool
and buy an old sofa that's terribly cool.

In winter I spruce up an old flaky fence
and buy a new ladder with my pounds and pence.

I clear my Gran's garden of thousands of weeds
and take some old windows she no longer needs.

All year I've worked hard and my muscles are sore,
but now I don't have to do jobs anymore.

Spring has set in and I've got what's required.
I invite my friends over and tell them they're hired!

We do hours and hours of smoothing and sawing,
putting in place all the walls and the flooring.

We work day and night, in all kinds of weather,
and within a few weeks it's all coming together!

Poppy plants flowers while Zoe checks shutters;
Eve paints the door while I clean the gutters.

By summer it's finished, completed, all done!
I invite my friends round for some sleepover fun.

It's all that I dreamed of; a palace for sure.
Somewhere I'm inspired to dream even more.

I knew it would happen; I knew I could do it!

I'll never give up once I set my mind to it.

The Women Who Inspired Claire

Claire dreamed of creating a space filled with all her favourite things, a place that she could share with her friends where they could all be inspired to dream. After putting her creative ideas together into an amazing floor plan, Claire worked tirelessly to build their treehouse sanctuary! Claire isn't the only girl who has had this dream. Some of the women below have been responsible for designing some of the most eye-catching buildings in the world. Others are working on innovative projects that will take architecture and design into the future. These are the girls who, like Claire, dared to dream that they could literally 'shape' the world – and grew into the women who helped to build it.

Hatshepsut

1507 BC – 1458 BC
ANCIENT EGYPT

Hatshepsut was the woman who was king. Since the word 'queen' in ancient Egyptian means 'wife of the king', Hatshepsut bore the male title to take the throne during the Eighteenth Dynasty. She is considered to have had one of the most peaceful reigns of any ancient Egyptian ruler. Hatshepsut was also one of Egypt's most successful builders, with her most exceptional piece being her memorial temple at Deir el-Bahri, which is considered one of the architectural wonders of the ancient world. Hatshepsut depicted herself in male dress, complete with fake beard, in many of the monuments in her temple. She did this connect herself to the male rulers who came before her to legitimise her power.

Florence Mary Taylor

'"Men make houses but women make homes." ...[W]e beg now to alter or amend [that old sentiment] slightly by adding "and houses too if they have the mind to."'

29 DECEMBER 1879 – 14 FEBRUARY 1969
UNITED KINGDOM

Florence worked with her father on his engineering projects until his death, when she was forced to find work to support herself and her two sisters. She decided to become a draftsman (creator of technical drawings such as blueprints), and trained at night school. After studying, she became the first female architect in Australia and had a successful working life town planning, designing and writing. Her achievements were so well publicised that women were empowered to enter into male-dominated industries.

Marion Mahony Griffin

'I'm the one who has to bring these drawings to life.'

14 FEBRUARY 1871 – 10 AUGUST 1961
UNITED STATES

Marion's contribution to designing numerous buildings is often unknown, as her work is frequently credited to fellow architect Frank Lloyd Wright. Marion's style was romantic: she was inspired by Japanese wood blocking prints and used watercolours to articulate her architectural vision. The portfolio she developed was the foundation of Frank's success, establishing him as an architectural genius. Marion rose to greater prominence later in her life when she moved to Australia, where her work included the design of several private residences and the Capitol Theatre in Melbourne.

Jane Drew

'It is no good building something that would be suitable for cold Northern Europe in Africa, where you need shade.'

24 MARCH 1911 – 27 JULY 1996
UNITED KINGDOM

As a child, Jane made tiny model buildings out of bricks and wood. She grew up to design grander buildings, including structures in Africa, India, the Middle East and London. Her goal was to create social change through architecture, as she believed good design empowered people to grow physically and spiritually through access to services such as education and health. She was one of Britain's most beloved architects for her ability to design structures that worked in harmony with their natural environments.

Dame Zaha Hadid

'I will never give myself the luxury of thinking "I've made it." I'm not the same as I was 20 years ago, but I always set the bar higher.'

31 October 1950 – 31 March 2016
IRAQ

Zaha was the innovative mind behind some of the world's most iconic buildings, including the London Olympic Aquatic Centre, the Guangzhou Opera House in China and the Sheikh Zayed Bridge in Abu Dhabi. She was known for her skill in contouring the buildings she constructed to their natural landscape. Not only was Zaha the first woman to receive the 2016 Royal Gold Medal for Architecture, she was also the first woman to be awarded the Pritzker Prize, which she received in 2004, and has received numerous other accolades.

Kazuyo Sejima

'As an architect, I feel it is part of our profession to use space as a medium to express our thoughts.'

29 October 1956 –
JAPAN

Kazuyo is a modernist architect who favours clean design that plays with cubes. She also enjoys fusing her designs with shiny materials, including glass, marble and metal. Kazuyo has designed some of the most innovative museums and public buildings in Japan, Europe and North America. Her unique vision has won her numerous awards and in 2010 Kazuyo became the first female Director of Architecture for the Architecture Biennale in Venice. In the same year, Kazuyo was the recipient of the prestigious Pritzker Architecture Prize – becoming only the second woman to receive the award.

Dr Cheong Koon Hean

'We need to pay more attention to public spaces, how to activate them so these are very friendly and people can congregate there… Don't forget the people.'

1957 –
SINGAPORE

Cheong is the CEO of the Housing and Development Board in Singapore, where she manages sustainable large-scale public housing projects. Cheong works to create communities in the residences she designs, where people can better interact and bond with each other. Cheong's effort to improve the quality of life for people living in affordable housing has made her the recipient of numerous awards, including the 2011 Women Who Make A Difference Award and the 2016 Lynn S. Beedle Lifetime Achievement Award.

Neri Oxman

'I believe in the balance between dreaming and building, problem seeking and problem solving, questioning and answering.'

1976 –
ISRAEL

Neri designs buildings to be informed by and work with their natural environment. Coining her innovative brand 'Material Ecology', Neri crosses science and technology with design to create evolutionary architecture that can not only respond to its environment by being biodegradable, but in some cases contains living matter to adapt to and interact with its natural surroundings! Her revolutionary work has made her one of the most awarded contemporary architects working today.